Maggie, Ma... and the Magic Magnifying Glass

Discover what's living inside YOUR mouth!

Written and Illustrated by

Dr. Doug Kekkonen, D.D.S.

"Thank you!" to the dedicated teachers who have been such an important part of my life, especially to the most talented teacher I know, my wife, Cynthie. I am grateful for her sharing with me a love of children's literature, children and grandchildren to enjoy it with, as well as unending support and encouragement. Thanks to Lindsay, too!

QUANTITY PURCHASES: Schools, companies, professional groups, clubs, and other organizations may qualify for special terms when ordering in quantities of this title. For information, email d.kekkonen@comcast.net.

EWWUH!!

Maggie and Marshall
were pretty grossed
out by something they
had just discovered.
Perhaps you'll think it's
disgusting too.

Maggie and Marshall are twins and the youngest members of the proud Gator family.

Their mom, Ali Gator, is a well respected attorney. She's known as the "litigator."

Their father, Ollie Gator, owns a successful pest control business. Folks call him the "fumigator."

Grandma, Ella Gator, is retired; but, she once guided expeditions into the far reaches of the seven seas. She's the "Navigator."

Grandpa, Al Gator, is retired too. Maggie and Marshall call him "Papa."

But, as he likes to tell it, he was once known to be slyest of the sly, wisest of the wise, solver of all mysteries big and small, super detective, respected world-wide as THE Investigator. Papa also likes to tell everyone how very smart and curious Maggie and Marshall are. He claims they got their curiosity and intelligence mostly from him.

On the day Maggie and Marshall got so grossed out, their curiosity had led them on an adventure into the dimly lit, spider web-decorated attic of Grandma and Papa's big, old house.

"Look at this weird magnifying glass," said Marshall. "I bet it was Papa's from when he was a detective."

"Yeah," agreed Maggie. "Let's go ask him how it works!"

"Ah-h-h, my Magic Magnifying Glass. I haven't seen this trusty, old friend in years," Papa said. "This rascal has some amazing powers. It was extremely valuable back when I was a detective."

"Yeah, when you were the slyest of the sly, wisest of the wise, solver of all mysteries big and small, super detective, respected world-wide as THE Investigator," Marshall recited proudly.

"Papa, what exactly does a detective do?"

"Well, young lady, you just did something that keeps us detectives busy; you asked a question," Papa said. "It can be a 'who,' a 'what,' a 'when,' a 'where,' a 'why,' or a 'how'; but, a detective's work always starts with a question. Then we go about finding the answers using the powers of science, the powers of our brains, and last, but certainly not least, the powers of observation.

That's where my Magic Magnifying Glass comes in handy."

"Please Papa, show us how it works," pleaded Maggie.

"I'm not sure if this old thing still does work, but we'll give it a try," Papa said. "First, let us start with a question."

"I have a 'why' question," said Marshall. "Why do mom and dad bug us so much about brushing our teeth?"

"Oh yeah!" agreed Maggie. "We hear it morning and night: 'brush your teeth,' 'brush your teeth!'"

"It is so annoying!" insisted Marshall. "'Don't forget to brush your teeth!' 'Did you brush your teeth?' 'Maggie and Marshall make sure you brush before you go to bed!'"

"'Don't forget, brush after breakfast,'" added Maggie.
"'Brush your teeth.'

'Brush your teeth.'

'Brush your teeth.'"

"'BRUSH YOUR TEETH!'"

the twins shouted as one.

"What's the big whoop about brushing our teeth?" asked Marshall.

"So, yes, what is the big whoop about brushing your teeth?" Papa said. "There's our question to investigate."

Then he asked, "How do you think we can use my Magic Magnifying Glass to help answer that question?"

"I guess we can look in our mouths to see if there's anything in there that needs to be brushed off," said Marshall.

"We could look for germs too," suggested Maggie. "I heard mouths have a bazillion germs."

"Here Maggie, look in my mouth," Marshall
handed her the magnifying glass and opened wide.

"Hmmmm. I see little pieces of food and some light-colored, fuzzy-looking gunk on your teeth," reported Maggie.

"That is a sticky material called 'plaque' which collects on your teeth when you don't brush," said Papa. "You must look very closely to see it because it is nearly the same color as your teeth."

"I don't see any germs. But, aren't germs really, really, really small? So small that we can't see them with a regular magnifying glass?" asked Maggie.

"Correct, but that is no 'regular magnifying glass,'" Papa reminded them. "Crank it up to 'Microscope Mode.'"

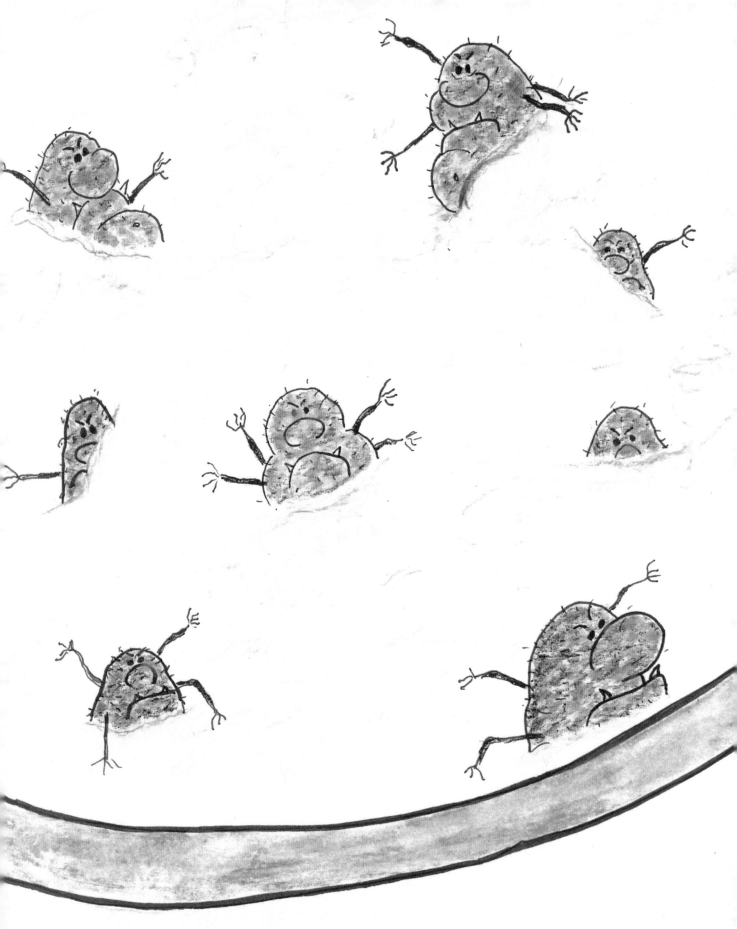

"Whoa!!" gasped Maggie. "Look at all the weird, ugly, bug-looking thingies everywhere! Are those germs?"

"Yes, we also call those slimy creatures 'bacteria,' and scientists tell us that we have billions of them in our mouths," Papa added. "Not all germs are bad for us; some are actually helpful."

"Let me look at your teeth with that, Maggie," said Marshall. "You have germs all over in your mouth too. And look, there's a bunch of grubby-looking ones hiding in the plaque. It looks like they're eating candy and drinking soda pop."

"Oh, yes," said Papa. "The mouth germs that hide in plaque just love, love, love sugary foods!"

"If germs are hanging out in the plaque on our teeth... eating and drinking sweets all day long... don't they ever have to... go to the bathroom?" asked Maggie.

"Well, yes, kind of," Papa said.

"YUCK!" yelled Marshall. "Germs are pooping and peeing in my mouth?"

"EEEWW!!" gagged Maggie.

"Disgusting, isn't it? The germs that live in plaque are nasty. When you eat sweet, sugary foods, you're feeding those awful germs exactly what they like best. They eat the sugar and make an acid waste that they dump right there in your mouth. So, it's kind of like they're going to the bathroom," Papa explained. "The worst part is that those hurtful acids can make holes in your teeth, make your gums bleed and give you bad breath."

"Now I get it," said Maggie.

"Me too," agreed Marshall.

"So, Investigators Maggie and Marshall, what is your conclusion?" asked Papa. "Why is brushing your teeth so important?"

"I don't want filthy germs doing nasty stuff in my mouth!" insisted Maggie. "We need to brush everyday to get the plaque off our teeth 'cause that's where the icky germs live!"

"Yeah!" said Marshall. "I don't want those dirty, stinkin', bad germs making holes in my teeth, making my gums bleed or giving me bad breath!"

"Maggie and Marshall did a great job answering their 'why is tooth brushing so important?' question by using observations, scientific knowledge, and their brains. They figured out that if you don't give them a place to live or feed them what they like, then bad germs won't be making yours a potty mouth. Wouldn't you agree that Maggie and Marshall are very smart?"

"Just like their Papa!"

About the Author

Doug Kekkonen, the author and illustrator, has always loved sharing the "magic" found in books with his children and now grandchildren. This, along with several other factors, is significant in his writing *Maggie, Marshall and the Magic Magnifying Glass*. Dr. Kekkonen had practiced family dentistry for 20 years when rheumatoid arthritis led him to seek another career. After attending the University of Colorado at Denver Teacher Education Program, he became a certified elementary teacher and taught in public schools for 14 years. Experiences in both of these careers also contribute much to this book. It is the author's hope that it will entertain, inform, and motivate.

Made in the USA
Charleston, SC
09 January 2016